Mechanical Connections

D1538548

Using Your Training Program

This is a comprehensive videotape/text training program. It may be used for independent self-study, or in a traditional classroom setting.

The videotapes are divided into segments, varying in length from four to six minutes.

This workbook is also divided into segments that generally correspond to the videotape segments.

Throughout the workbook, you will find symbols that will help you to identify how the information is organized:

Objective
Goal

Application
Doing
Hands-On

Self-Check
Review Questions
Pre/Post Test

Bibliography
Reference/Standard

Calculator
Exercises
Computation

Concept/Idea
Understanding
Theory

Closer Look
More Information

You may alternately view a segment of videotape and read the corresponding segment in your workbook. A variety of questions and practical exercises are provided to further your understanding of the subject.

If you are undertaking your training in a classroom setting, your instructor will administer a pretest and a post test during the course. Final evaluation of your progress through the training program will be based on a combination of test scores and observation of your performance during hands-on exercises.

Student Workbook

Contents

Student Workbook

Overview

The training program, *Mechanical Connections*, discusses the importance of maintaining and installing mechanical connections in instrumentation and control loops and describes how various types of connections are made. Information on tubing materials and applications, the tasks necessary to install a tubing run, and the procedures for cutting and bending tubing are discussed at length. The function and parts of fittings, such as compression fittings and flared fittings, and descriptions of the methods and tools used to install fittings on metal and plastic tubing are provided. A procedure for silver soldering connections is also included.

Prerequisites

Mechanical Connections is designed for persons interested in basic instrumentation and control. Since this is an introductory program, there are no specific prerequisites for this study. However, it is recommended that students successfully complete the study of *Electrical Connections* in the ITTP/2 series. An understanding of basic physics and math will also be helpful.

Gaskets and O-Rings

1. Describe the importance of mechanical connections in instrumentation and control loops.
2. Identify types of gasket materials.
3. Demonstrate removal and replacement of a gasket.
4. Demonstrate removal and replacement of an O-ring.

Tubing

5. Identify examples of tubing applications in instrument systems.
6. Identify kinds of tubing materials and their applications.
7. Calculate tubing gain.
8. Demonstrate how to cut tubing.
9. Demonstrate how to deburr tubing.
10. Identify three types of tubing benders.
11. Demonstrate how to cut and bend tubing.

Fittings and Plastic Tubing

12. Identify the parts of a compression fitting.
13. Demonstrate how to flare a fitting.
14. Identify the types of plastic tubing.
15. Demonstrate how to install plastic tubing.
16. Demonstrate how to check for leaks in a tubing installation.

Silver Soldering

17. Demonstrate how to deburr a hacksaw cut.
18. Demonstrate how to clean tubings and fittings for silver soldering.
19. Demonstrate how to silver solder a fitting to tubing.
20. Explain the importance of cleaning connections after silver soldering.

Segment 1

The primary functions of the instruments in a control loop are measurement, comparison, and taking appropriate action. The response of a control loop is determined by several factors: the accuracy of the measurements, the action of the controller, and the response of the final control element. In addition to the instruments, all of the components in the loop as well as the integrity of their associated fittings and connections ensure the quality of measurement and control.

To communicate, instruments must have uninterrupted paths of transmission. A break in any connection within the loop may distort the signals being transmitted or cause a loss of signal. Thus, in order to ensure that control loops function properly, it is essential to install and maintain connections correctly.

Describe the importance of mechanical connections in instrumentation and control loops.

Mechanical connections usually have seals, such as gaskets or O-rings, to prevent leakage between rigid metal parts. Gaskets help fill imperfections between irregular mating surfaces. Because gaskets can be compressed, they form a tight seal between mating surfaces. Instrument gaskets are generally small and can easily be compressed to form a tight seal.

Identify types of gasket materials.

Gaskets are made from a variety of natural or synthetic materials, such as rubber, metal, and cork. The primary selection factor for gaskets that are in contact with process material is compatibility with that material. Rubber gaskets are often appropriate for low-temperature, low-pressure air or water applications. Synthetic materials are more appropriate for high temperatures or corrosive process materials. Cork gaskets are primarily used in low-pressure gas or oil applications.

Demonstrate removal and replacement of a gasket.

Assuming that the gasket in place was properly selected, a replacement gasket should always be identical to the gasket in use. The specific steps to follow when removing and replacing gaskets usually depend on the type of gasket and its application. Replacement gaskets are usually supplied by the manufacturer.

Gaskets and O-Rings

When a gasket is being removed, instrument air ports should be covered with caps, if they are available, to prevent particles of the old gasket from entering them, and care should be taken to scrape or wipe the particles of the old gasket away from the openings. Old gaskets should be removed with scrapers or other special tools to avoid nicking or scratching the instrument gasket surface. Nicks or scratches will prevent the new gasket from forming a good seal. After the old gasket has been removed, the instrument gasket surface should be cleaned with a cloth and facility-approved solvent. The new gasket can then be installed. As the instrument is being reassembled, the screws or bolts should be tightened in sequence to distribute compression evenly around the gasket.

Demonstrate removal and replacement of an O-ring.

O-rings also form tight seals between rigid metal parts. O-rings are often used to seal pneumatic instrument connections. As with gaskets, O-rings are manufactured in a variety of materials. Again, the primary selection factor for O-ring materials is compatibility with the application. Unlike gaskets, O-rings are usually installed in grooves rather than between flat surfaces. The O-ring normally protrudes from the groove. When another surface is brought in contact with the O-ring, the O-ring compresses to form a seal. In some applications, O-rings may be lubricated to increase their sealing ability and to facilitate their installation.

Take care to protect the surface of the instrument when replacing an O-ring. There are special tools available that are designed to stretch an O-ring and lift it from its groove. After the O-ring is out of the groove, it can usually be removed by hand. The groove should be cleaned with a facility-approved solvent to prepare it for the installation of the new O-ring. In most cases, the O-ring must be lubricated and stretched to fit over the instrument surface and into the groove. The O-ring must be handled carefully to protect it from damage that might prevent a tight seal. Threaded fittings can be a special problem because they often have sharp edges that can cut into the O-ring as it is being installed. One way to eliminate this problem is to place a plastic cap over the threads to protect the O-ring. Inspect the O-ring to be sure it is completely seated within the groove and was not damaged during installation. Then, tighten the O-ring connection, but do not overtighten. As it is compressed, the O-ring should seal any imperfections in the connection.

Gaskets and O-Rings

Schedules for replacing gaskets and O-rings vary according to facility practices. In many facilities, gaskets are changed when they fail. However, some facilities routinely replace gaskets when the plant schedules downtime. In most cases, O-rings are replaced each time an instrument is disassembled because once an O-ring has been compressed, it may not seal properly and should not be reused.

Hands-On Exercises

1. Familiarize yourself with the various types of gaskets and O-rings used in your facility, and review the correct installation and removal of each type.

2. Determine which types of gasket and O-ring materials are compatible with the different types of processes in your facility.

Review Questions

1. Leaking connections can cause distorted or lost _____ within the loop preventing communication between instruments.

2. True or False. Optimal instrument performance is far more important to the proper operation of a loop than the performance of components, such as plastic tubing, that are easily replaced.

3. What is the primary function of gaskets and O-rings?

4. True or False. The materials of which mechanical seals are made must be compatible with the process materials of the applications in which they are used.

5. _____ are installed in grooves to create a mechanical seal.

6. _____ are installed between flat surfaces to create a mechanical seal.

Segment 2

Identify examples of tubing applications in instrument systems.

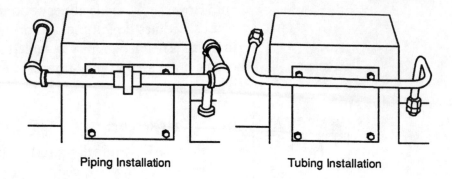

Piping Installation   Tubing Installation

Metal or plastic tubing has many applications in instrumentation systems. For example, it may be used to connect instruments to process piping, or carry pneumatic signals, or supply air to pneumatic instruments. Tubing is usually lighter in weight, more flexible, less bulky, and easier to install compared to piping with the same pressure and flow rating. Also, in piping installations, a pipe fitting is usually required each time the piping changes direction. Tubing is much easier to bend, so relatively fewer connections are needed. Fewer connections mean less potential for leaks.

Identify kinds of tubing materials and their applications.

Tubing is manufactured from many different materials with a wide selection of pressure ratings. In addition to the requirements of the process and the operating environment, corrosion, temperature, and stress, must be considered when selecting tubing for an application.

Stainless steel tubing is corrosion-resistant and can withstand high temperatures and pressures. Copper tubing is not as strong as steel, but copper tubing provides more flexibility. Copper tubing is often found in systems with relatively low operating pressures and temperatures, such as pneumatic signal lines. Plastic tubing is neither as strong nor as heat-resistant as metal tubing; however, it does have significant advantages, such as flexibility and ease of installation. Plastic tubing is often found in low-pressure pneumatic applications.

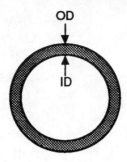

Facility specifications provide detailed information on the types of tubing approved for each application. Specifications may also indicate the size required. Tubing size is usually expressed in inside diameter (ID) and outside diameter (OD). The inside and outside diameters of the tubing determine the wall thickness. In addition to corrosion, temperature, and stress, selection factors that determine the appropriate type of tubing for a given application are process compatibility, flow requirements, pressure, and the velocity of the fluid to be carried.

Successful tubing installations require careful observation and planning. First, determine the best path for the tubing. Remember to consider the maintenance that will be required for the system. Ensure that the route does not block access to nearby pumps, valves, and other process equipment. Also, make certain that the tubing path allows sufficient clearance from any adjacent high-temperature or high-pressure areas. The route should never interfere with walkways or block doors.

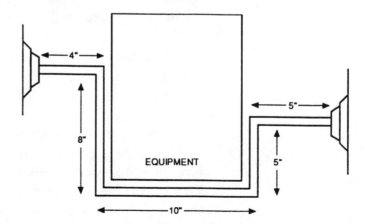

After determining the best path, sketch the layout of the planned installation, recording the necessary dimensions. Note the number of tubing fittings required. Any supports necessary for the tubing should also be included in the sketch. The number and location of supports required will depend on the size and wall thickness of the tubing. If valves, regulators, or other instruments are to be connected to the tubing, note their position. In applications in which temperature variations are expected, consider the use of expansion loops. Expansion loops prevent stress by allowing sufficient room for the tubing to expand or contract if either process temperature or ambient temperature fluctuates.

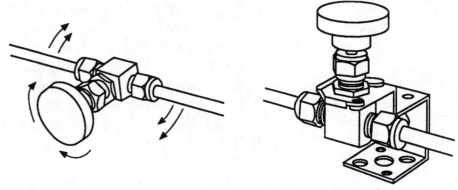

Unsupported Valve   Properly Supported Valve

All interconnected components must be securely mounted to avoid stress on the tubing after it has been installed. Factors to consider when determining how much support is required include the length of the tubing run, the size of the tubing, the tubing material, and the weight and flow rate of the fluid that will flow through the tubing. Valves should be properly supported to prevent stressing the tubing when they are operated.

Accurate measurements should be taken when planning to install tubing. Taking measurements can be difficult when there are obstacles in the tubing path or when the instruments to be connected are on different planes. One method of measuring between two instruments located at the same height is to insert two pieces of tubing into the instrument fittings to serve as guides. A level should be used to check that the guides are properly aligned. Then, a rule can be placed across the guides to measure the actual distance. The measurement should be made from the center of one fitting to the center of the other. Each distance should be recorded on the installation diagram immediately after the measurement has been taken.

Measurements between 90-degree bends in the tubing should be made at right angles, using levels, adjustable squares, or plumb bobs. For example, in a horizontal measurement, a rule should be aligned at a 90-degree angle with a combination square. If the fittings being measured are not at the same height, it is best to determine a common reference point, such as a wall, and measure the distance from that point to each fitting. The distance from each fitting to the bend must also be measured.

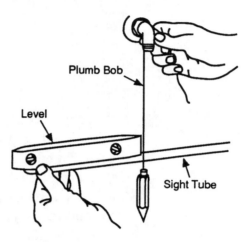

For a vertical tubing run, use a plumb bob to ensure that measurements are made at right angles. A plumb bob suspended from the center of a vertical fitting can help to determine where a 90-degree bend should be made.

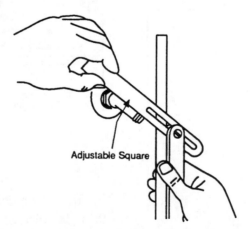

When bends other than 90 degrees must be made, an adjustable square can be used to determine the required angle of the bend. The angle indicated on the adjustable square is the angle at which the tubing should be bent.

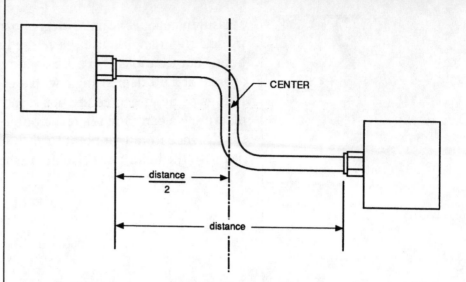

If the tubing is to be centered between two fittings, a straight edge can be placed perpendicular to one fitting. Then, the distance from the straight edge to the other fitting is measured. The sum of this distance is divided in half to locate the center between the two fittings. The total distance is the distance from the fitting to the bend plus the length of the tubing that will be inserted into the fitting. After these measurements have been recorded for one fitting, the same procedure is used to take the measurements for the other fitting.

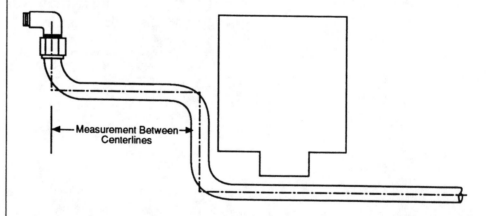

Tubing measurements are often made from centerline to centerline of tubing for installations that include a bend. This allows the measurements to coincide with the markings on the tubing bender. If existing tubing is being replaced, the old piece of tubing can sometimes be used as a pattern. Be careful to remove the tubing pattern so as not to distort it.

Several good methods are used to measure tubing, and some facilities have a preferred method. Correctly measuring the amount of tubing will always indicate a slight amount more tubing than is actually needed because tubing measurements are based on square corners. Actual installations have bends that require less tubing. However, it is difficult to estimate precisely how much less that will be.

Calculate tubing gain.

The exact amount of tubing gained through a bend depends on the size of the tubing and its angles. Manufacturers generally supply tables to simplify the calculations. Gain factors may also be marked on the handles of some tube benders.

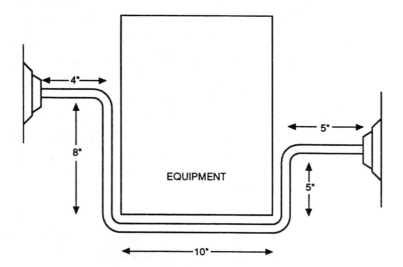

The measurements for this installation are 4 inches, 8 inches, 10 inches, 5 inches, and 5 inches, respectively. The total run is 32 inches. As shown in the illustration, four bends are needed. Assume the gain on the bender used for this task is 0.66. This amount is multiplied by 4, the number of bends required, to calculate the actual amount of tubing gained through the bends. The amount of gain, 2.64, is then subtracted from 32, the total run, to determine the amount of tubing to cut for the installation. In this example, the actual amount of tubing required is 29.36 inches or 2.445 feet. Remember that calculations will vary. However, accurate measurements can be obtained if the reference table selected is designed for the size of the tubing and the type of bender being used.

Demonstrate how to cut tubing.

Tubing that is handled properly will provide long, useful service. When preparing to cut a length of tubing, hold it flat with one hand and unroll it with the other. Copper tubing is manufactured to close tolerances and can be easily damaged if it is not handled carefully. Pulling on copper tubing may cause it to stretch or kink. Enough tubing should be uncoiled to permit it to lie flat at the point where it will be cut. Uncoiling too much tubing should be avoided as it can adversely affect the temper of the metal, causing it to become brittle. Mark the place where the length of tubing is to be cut without scratching the metal.

For most types of tubing, use a tubing cutter with an adjustable blade. The free end of the tubing should be supported as the cut is made. The cutter is placed around the tubing, and the blade is aligned with the mark. Then, the blade is tightened until it rests firmly against the tubing. At this point, the blade can be rotated around the tubing using a smooth circular motion. It may be necessary to tighten the blade at intervals to make certain that it rests against the surface of the tube. Using a tubing cutter provides a significant advantage over other cutting tools. Tubing cutters make a square cut. Square cuts are necessary for most types of fittings and connections.

Demonstrate how to deburr tubing.

A disadvantage of using a tube cutter is that tube cutters may create burrs on the inside of tubing. Burrs must be removed to prevent them from restricting flow and possibly interfering with proper tubing installation. Reamers and scrapers are tools that can be used to remove burrs. Care should be taken not to reduce the wall thickness as burrs are removed. Otherwise, the tubing might be weakened. Filings that result from deburring should be removed before bending the tubing.

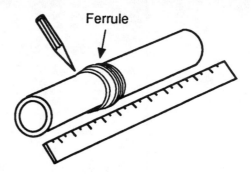

Ferrule

A correctly sized ferrule or sleeve can be slipped over the tubing to provide a guide to make a mark around the circumference of the tubing. Marks that extend completely around the tubing at the appropriate point for the bend can be seen regardless of how the tubing is positioned in the bender. It is also helpful to develop a system for marking the direction of the bend. One method of indicating direction is to make a lengthwise mark on the tubing. This mark should be positioned on the portion of the tubing that will be the outside of the bend. It is easy to mistake the direction of the bend on a complicated tubing installation. Keeping the installation sketch handy at all times helps avoid confusion.

Identify three types of tubing benders.

Several types and sizes of tubing benders are designed for use in different applications. In all cases, the bender must fit the outside diameter of the tubing. Otherwise, benders can be divided into two major categories: hand benders and production benders. Examples of hand benders include spring benders and compression benders. Production benders are found in shops. These types of benders are used to produce accurate bends on piping or larger tubing. The torque required to make the bend is provided by gears or hydraulic power.

A spring bender is a spring coil that fits over the tubing as it is bent. The spring helps to protect the tubing from being kinked or flattened as it is bent. Unlike some of the other types of benders available, spring benders usually do not have degree markings for the angles. It is necessary to estimate the proper angle before making the bend.

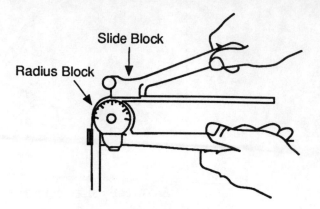

Slide Block

Radius Block

Compression benders are frequently used to bend metal tubing. This type of bender has a stationary radius block and a movable side block. Around the outside of the radius block is a groove that supports the tubing as it is bent. There are markings on both blocks. The radius block has numbers marked on it to indicate the angle of the bend. The slide block has marks that are used to properly align the tubing in the bender.

Demonstrate how to bend tubing.

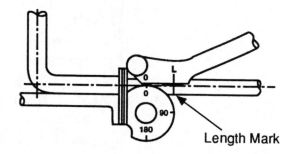

Length Mark

The markings on compression benders make them relatively easy to use. To begin, the zero on the slide block must be aligned with the zero on the radius block. The tubing is then inserted in the slide block groove until the line marked L on the slide block is aligned with the mark placed on the tubing to indicate where the bend should be. To ensure that the bend will be made in the right direction, center the direction mark in the slide block groove. Finally, move the slide block around the tubing until the zero on the slide block is aligned with the proper degree mark on the radius block. This movement creates the first bend.

The tubing should be left in the bender while preparations are made to make the next bend. The distance between the first bend and the second must be measured. A T-square is a good tool for this purpose. Once the rule is aligned with the edge of the radius block, it should be kept parallel to the tubing while measuring the distance to the next bend. Again, the ferrule can be used to mark the center for the second bend. Once this is done, the tubing is repositioned in the bender, and the second bend is made. After all of the bends shown in the sketch have been made, reposition the tubing and take the final measurement. Make the final cut with the tubing cutter. More often than not, there will be slightly more length remaining after the last bend than is required because bends require less tubing than square corners. After the excess has been cut away, any burrs remaining should be removed. The tubing can then be installed in the instrument system.

A good tubing bend has no flattening of the tubing through the bend. However, if tools are used improperly, a poor bend may result. Some symptoms of a poor bend include flattening, kinking, and wrinkling. Poorly bent tubing should not be installed in a system because a bad bend can weaken the tubing or restrict flow.

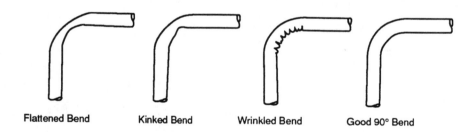

Flattened Bend   Kinked Bend   Wrinkled Bend   Good 90° Bend

Hands-On Exercises

1. Take time to study the connections in the instrument systems in your facility. Note which types of tubing materials are used and the relative sizes found in different loops.

2. Try to correlate the use of specific tubing materials with the various process materials produced in your facility. Also identify the process characteristics that demand special sizes or materials or expansion loops.

Tubing

Review Questions

1. Bends require (more/less) tubing than square corners.

2. _____ compensate for temperature fluctuations in a control loop.

3. What are the dimensions that determine the wall thickness of tubing?

4. What type of tubing material has the characteristics needed for high-temperature, high-pressure applications that require a corrosion-resistant material?

5. _____ should be removed from tubing to minimize flow restriction.

Segment 3

Due to their reliability and the ease with which they can be installed, compression fittings are widely used in industry. Compression fittings can also be removed and reconnected without damaging either the fitting or the process tubing. A variety of compression fittings are designed for use in process applications. Flared fittings are restricted to applications with metal tubing. Compression fittings may be used on either metal or plastic tubing.

Identify the parts of a compression fitting.

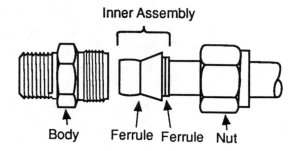

The parts of compression fittings common to most types are an inner body, usually consisting of a ferrule arrangement, a fitting body that holds the parts of the inner assembly together, and a nut that threads to the fitting body. As the nut is tightened, the parts that make up the inside assembly compress the tubing, forcing it slightly out of shape.

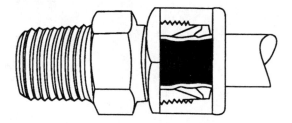

In order to obtain a good seal, a specific degree of compression must be achieved. The installation instructions that accompany most compression fittings specify the number of turns required to ensure the right amount of compression. For example, the instructions may specify one and one-quarter turns with a wrench after the fitting is made up hand-tight. With most compression fittings, the tubing is inserted until it butts up to the seat in the fitting body. The nut is then tightened until it is hand tight.

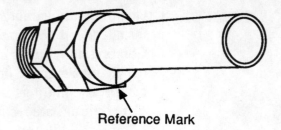

Reference Mark

Check the installation instructions to determine the number of turns specified by the manufacturer for a good seal. Tighten the nut the specified number of turns using the reference mark as a guide. Fittings are made to close tolerances. Try to insert a gap-inspection gage between the nut and the body of the fitting after it has been tightened. If the nut has been sufficiently tightened, the gage will not fit in the gap.

Demonstrate how to flare a fitting.

Good compression also ensures a good seal with flared fittings. The difference between compression fittings and flared fittings is that, with flared fittings, the end of the tubing is flared to provide a rim that the ferrule and body of the fitting seal against.

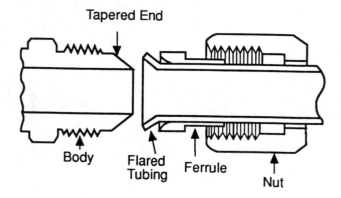

Tapered End

Body   Flared Tubing   Ferrule   Nut

As illustrated, the parts of a flared fitting include the body, which has a tapered end, the ferrule that holds the flared tubing, and the fitting nut that is used to tighten the assembled parts. In a flared fitting, the ferrule forms the seal on the tubing by forcing the prepared (flared) edge up against the tapered end of the fitting body. The nut compresses the parts to form the seal.

As with compression fittings, the manufacturer's instructions explain how to obtain a good seal. As with most tasks, the first step is to select the necessary tools. Since the tubing must be flared, it is necessary to determine the correct angle for the fitting and locate the appropriate flaring tool for the job. Most flaring tools consist of a die block, a cone-shaped flaring pin, and a yoke.

To install the fitting, the ferrule and the nut must be slipped over clean, deburred tubing. The tubing end is then placed in the die block flush with the surface of the die block on the funnel side. Once it is positioned properly, the yoke is placed on the die block and the cone is aligned with the tubing. Many yokes have a T-shaped handle that is easy to grasp. The yoke handle is tightened just enough to seat the die block, cone, and tubing. Care should be taken not to overtighten as overtightening could damage the tubing. After loosening the yoke handle, the yoke and die handle can be removed, and the flare can be checked.

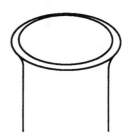

Pock Marks Caused   Split Flare   Good Flare
By Chips or Filings

If there are any signs of damage, such as pits from filings, or if the tubing is split, it should be rejected. If the flare looks satisfactory, the next step is to check that the nut and ferrule fit properly. If the fit is acceptable, the body can be installed and the fitting nut can be tightened. This pulls the ferrule and the fitting body in contact with the flare on the tubing to form a good seal.

Plastic tubing is often used for pneumatic signal lines between instruments. Factors that must be evaluated when selecting plastic tubing include (1) the pressure that will be carried in the line; (2) the ambient and process temperatures; (3) compatibility with process materials; (4) any potentially damaging stress, such as tension on the line or vibration; and (5) the operating environment and the location of the installation.

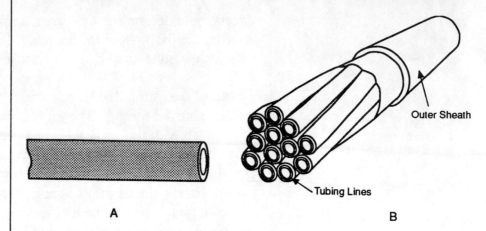

A   B

Identify the types of plastic tubing.

In some applications, a single plastic tube is used; for other applications with multiple signals and connections, a bundle of single tubes within a single protective sheath may be appropriate. Because plastic tubing is not as strong as metal tubing, it must be supported in long runs and protected in areas where it could be damaged. However, plastic tubing is significantly easier to install because it is light and flexible. As with metal tubing, specifications for the proper size and type of plastic tubing for an installation will be indicated on facility piping diagrams.

Demonstrate how to install plastic tubing.

As with other types of tubing, determine the appropriate path for the tubing, and measure to find the approximate length required for the run. In some instances, such as with short runs, it may be possible to rely on a visual estimate. In either case, it is good practice to allow for a little slack. Then, the tubing end should be cut as squarely as possible. A square cut helps to ensure a tight connection in the fitting. Compression fittings designed for use with plastic tubing differ from those for metal tubing. Often, the ferrules are made of plastic rather than metal, for example. The fitting body may also be made of plastic. Some fittings also have a tube support built into the end of the fitting. After the tubing has been prepared and inspected to be sure it is in good condition, the nut is removed from the fitting. The plastic tubing is inserted into the body of the fitting over the tubing support, if the fitting is so designed. The fitting nut is first tightened by hand, then to the number of specified turns with a tubing wrench.

Demonstrate how to check for leaks in a tubing installation.

All fittings must be checked for leaks after installation. Visual inspections will often reveal liquid leaks, but they are not adequate to determine if air leaks are present. Leak detector fluid will help locate air leaks. To determine if the fitting provides a tight seal, the air supply to the instrument should be turned on. After applying leak detector fluid to the connection, observe the connection carefully. The presence of air leaks is indicated by bubbles forming at the points where air is escaping. It usually only takes a few seconds before bubbles appear.

In most cases, the problem can be solved by tightening the connection slightly. Leak detector fluid should then be applied again to determine if the leak has been eliminated. If bubbles continue to form, the fitting should be removed and reinspected to determine if the leak is caused by internal damage to the fitting. If the fitting appears to be in good condition, it can be reinstalled. Check for leaks, again. If no bubbles appear, the instrument can be returned to service.

Hands-On Exercises

1. Identify the types of fittings used to connect metal and plastic tubing to instruments in control loops in your facility. Examine the parts of fittings to determine how they fit together to form a good seal.

2. Familiarize yourself with the tools used to make connections and learn how to use them properly.

Review Questions

1. True or False. Compression fittings achieve a tight seal by forcing the flared edge of the tubing up against the tapered end of the fitting body.

2. Flared tubing should be rejected if there are signs of damage such as a _____ or _____ on the flare.

3. Plastic ferrules may be found in (compression/flared) fittings for plastic tubing.

4. True or False. Compression fittings are commonly found on metal and plastic tubing.

5. _____ is essential when trying to locate air leaks in instrument connections.

Segment 4

In high-pressure applications, very strong connections are required and mechanical connections may not be adequate. An alternative is to silver solder the tubing joints. Silver solder forms a strong tight bond between two surfaces. Stainless steel is typically the material selected for tubing carrying fluids at high pressure and special solder-joint fittings are available for use in these applications.

Hacksaws are usually a good cutting tool for stainless steel. However, a hacksaw often creates burrs both inside and outside the tubing. As with any metal tubing, burrs that could interfere with a good seal must be removed before the tube can be silver soldered.

Demonstrate how to deburr a hacksaw cut.

Use reamers, scrapers, or round files to remove inside burrs. Outside burrs can be removed with a flat file. Holding the file at a 45-degree angle is effective. Light strokes with the file will remove most burrs with little difficulty. Care should be taken to prevent nicking or scratching the tubing with the file. After deburring the tubing and removing any filings that remain, the tubing can be prepared for soldering.

Demonstrate how to clean tubings and fittings for silver soldering.

Silver solder will not adhere to dirty or corroded surfaces. The fitting and the areas of the tubing to be soldered must be absolutely clean. The best way to clean the metal is to rub it with an emery cloth. Be sure to include the interior of the fitting and the inner and outer sections of the tubing   Emery is an abrasive that removes oxides created from exposure to air or moisture. The areas polished with the emery cloth will appear shiny when clean. After cleaning, wipe the areas with a lint-free cloth saturated with solvent to remove any oil deposits resulting from handling the tubing, and avoid touching the surfaces. To ensure good connections, the tubing should be soldered immediately after cleaning.

Demonstrate how to silver solder a fitting to tubing.

Flux helps silver solder flow and adhere to metal surfaces, such as stainless steel. Flux is designed for specific metals and temperatures, so it is necessary to select a flux compound that meets the requirements of each application. Flux should be applied immediately after cleaning the metal. An even coat of flux is applied to all of the surfaces to be soldered. The tubing and the fitting should be assembled while the flux is wet. The assembly should be supported while soldering to relieve any strain on the parts.

Silver soldering is done with a propane or oxygen-acetylene torch. Consequently, soldering can only be done in areas where it is permissible to use an open flame. *Silver soldering is never done in a potentially explosive environment.* Soldering is restricted to work areas in which only noncombustibles are present. Instruments near the soldering area should be protected from heat generated by the soldering torch.

After the torch is lit and the proper adjustments are made to the flame, the connection is heated. The torch should be centered over the point where the tubing and fitting are to be joined. Keep the flame moving slightly to ensure even heating and to prevent hot spots and burning. The flux should be watched carefully to determine when the correct temperature has been achieved. The connection will be ready to solder after the flux has turned from a white paste to a clear liquid.

Silver solders are manufactured with different percentages of silver. As with flux compounds, silver solder should be selected according to the requirements of each application. The solder should also be coated with flux before flame is applied to it. After coating the solder with flux, the solder is applied to the connection. The heat of the flame will draw the solder between the surfaces of the tubing and the fitting. The edges of the connection should be watched carefully. The soldering will be complete when a small ridge of silver solder, called a fillet, appears all the way around the connection. After the fillet has been formed, the joint will be sound. The tubing connection should then be allowed to cool at room temperature until it can be handled comfortably.

Explain the importance of cleaning connections after silver soldering.

Flux can corrode metal, so, it must be removed to protect the connection. Excess flux and the discoloration caused by soldering can be removed by scrubbing the connection with water and a wire brush. Care should be taken to see that both the inside and the exterior of the connection are clean. Check facility guidelines to determine the requirements that apply to returning instruments with silver-soldered connections to service.

Silver Soldering

It is understood that controllers and other advanced process instruments are essential for regulating operations and alerting control room personnel to system problems. However, the importance of gaskets, fittings, tubing, and other mechanical connections must also be properly evaluated. Without the less sophisticated components that connect instruments to processes or to other instruments, the more complex components could not operate efficiently and accurately. No matter how complex the process, its operation ultimately depends in part on the simple mechanical connections that link instruments together.

Mechanical connections often function reliably for long periods of time. Some components are replaced periodically; others are not replaced until they adversely affect the operation of the control loop. Nevertheless, equipment downtime caused by unscheduled maintenance and repair can be minimized through the implementation of fundamental work practices. Always follow manufacturers' instructions and facility guidelines when working with any instruments or components because operational principles and designs differ.

Fundamental work practices incorporate these concepts and strategies. Always make certain that the initial installation is done properly. Prepare each component of the connection carefully. Take the time to measure the tubing accurately and to cut it squarely. Clean the tubing or connections thoroughly. Always use the proper tools to avoid the risk of damaging the connection. Assemble the components according to the appropriate instructions and guidelines. Bench test connections to make sure they will be able to withstand normal operating conditions. Use facility-recommended methods to test for pressure or liquid leaks before installing instruments in the field.

Inspect connections during system start up. New connections should be examined thoroughly at this time because field testing is more reliable than bench testing. Providing that new connections function properly when first placed in service, it is reasonable to assume that they will be able to withstand the continuing demands of temperature, pressure, flow, and level requirements.

The work associated with preventive maintenance procedures should be done with the same care exercised during initial installations. Following the preventive maintenance schedule established for instruments, connections, tubing, and other process components also helps to reduce downtime for mechanical repairs, if the work is done properly.

During routine maintenance inspections, look for any changes in the instruments, their connections, or the processes that the instruments control. For example, be alert to any changes, malfunctions, or unexpected fluctuations in the system. Careful inspection may also reveal new or previously undetected liquid or air leaks or other signs of damage or corrosion. Note these problems and report them so that prompt corrective action can be taken. Early detection often makes it possible to implement relatively simple solutions. In addition to ensuring the reliable performance of process control systems, effective work practices also increase personal satisfaction and productivity.

Hands-On Exercises

1. Identify the control loops that require silver-soldered connections in your facility. Discuss what types of silver solder and flux are used to make these connections with personnel who have soldering experience.

2. Study your facility's procedures for silver soldering connections and familiarize yourself with the equipment and tools used for this work. Identify the areas in which soldering is permitted in your facility.

Review Questions

1. Metals that are to be soldered must be thoroughly cleaned (before/after) flux is applied.

2. True or False. Body oil transferred to fittings from normal handling can interfere or prevent the solder from making a strong joint.

3. (Emery cloths/Wire brushes) can be used to remove flux and discoloration from a fitting after a joint has been made.

4. (Hacksaws/Tubing cutters) are preferred cutting tools for stainless steel tubing.

Silver Soldering

5. The use of (hacksaws/tubing cutters) usually creates burrs on the inside and the outside of stainless steel tubing.

6. True or False. Universal flux and silver solder are one-purpose mediums that can be used on any soldering application.

7. Flux residue can cause stainless steel tubing to (discolor/corrode).

8. _____ is a good tool for removing dirt, corrosion, and other residue from fittings and tubing before solder is applied.

Review Questions — Gaskets and O-Rings

1. Leaking connections can cause distorted or lost signals within the loop preventing communication between instruments.

2. False. Instrument signals are continuous through most control loops, so all parts of the loop, including fittings, wiring, tubing, and other types of connections are just as important to process measurement and control as instruments are.

3. What is the primary function of gaskets and O-rings?

   Gaskets and O-rings form mechanical seals between rigid metal parts.

4. True. The materials of which mechanical seals are made must be compatible with the process materials of the applications in which they are used.

5. O-rings are installed in grooves to create a mechanical seal.

6. Gaskets are installed between flat surfaces to create a mechanical seal.

Review Questions — Tubing

1. Bends require less tubing than square corners.

2. Expansion loops compensate for temperature fluctuations in a control loop.

3. What are the dimensions that determine the wall thickness of tubing?

   The dimensions that determine the wall thickness of tubing are its inside and outside diameters.

4. What type of tubing material has the characteristics needed for high-temperature, high-pressure applications that require a corrosion-resistant material?

   Stainless steel tubing is corrosion-resistant and suitable for high-temperature, high-pressure applications.

5. Burrs should be removed from tubing to minimize flow restriction.

Review Questions — Fittings and Plastic Tubing

1. False. Flared fittings achieve a tight seal by forcing the flared edge of the tubing up against the tapered end of the fitting body.

2. Flared tubing should be rejected if there are signs of damage such as a split or pock marks on the flare.

3. Plastic ferrules may be found in compression fittings for plastic tubing.

4. True. Compression fittings are commonly found on metal and plastic tubing.

5. Leak detector fluid is essential when trying to locate air leaks in instrument connections.

Review Questions — Silver Soldering

1. Metals that are to be soldered must be thoroughly cleaned before flux is applied.

2. True. Body oil transferred to fittings from normal handling can interfere or prevent the solder from making a strong joint.

3. Wire brushes can be used to remove flux and discoloration from the fitting after a joint has been made.

4. Hacksaws are preferred cutting tools for stainless steel tubing.

5. The use of hacksaws usually creates burrs on the inside and the outside of stainless steel tubing.

6. False. Flux compounds and silver solder are available in many different forms and must be selected specifically for a given soldering application.

7. Flux residue can cause stainless steel tubing to corrode.

8. Emery cloth is a good tool for removing dirt, corrosion, and other residue from fittings and tubing before solder is applied.

Burr   A thin, turned-over edge or fin produced by a grinding wheel, cutting tool, or punch.

Ferrule   A tapered bushing used in compression-type tubing fittings to provide the wedging action that creates a mechanical seal.

Fitting   An auxiliary part of standard size and configuration that can be used to facilitate assembly; in constructing a system of pipe or tubing, for example, connections are more easily made if standard elbows, tees, unions, and couplings are used to connect straight lengths of pipe, rather than bending the pipe or making special preparations before welding lengths of pipe together.

Gasket   A sealing member, usually made by stamping from a sheet of cork, rubber, metal or impregnated sealing material and clamped between two essentially flat surfaces to prevent pressurized fluid from leaking through the crevice; typical applications include flanged joints in piping, head seals in a reciprocating engine or compressor, casing seals in a pump, or virtually anywhere a pressure-tight joint is needed between two stationary members. Also known as a static seal.

ID   Abbreviation for inside diameter.

Inside diameter   The maximum dimension across a cylindrical or spherical cavity. Ideally, this is a line passing through the exact center of the cavity and perpendicular to the cavity's inner surface.

Joint   A separable or inseparable juncture between two or more materials.

O-ring   A torroidal sealing ring made of synthetic rubber or similar material. The cross section through the torus is usually round or oval, but may be rectangular or some other shape.

OD   Abbreviation for outside diameter.

Outside diameter   The outer dimension of a circular member, such as a rod, pipe, or tube.

Seal   1. Any device or system that creates a nonleaking union between two mechanical components. 2. A perfectly tight closure or joint.

Silver solder

A brazing alloy composed of silver, copper, and zinc that melts at a temperature below that of silver but above that of lead-tin solder.

Static Seal

See **gasket**.

Tube

A long hollow cylinder used for conveying fluids or transmitting pressure. Also known as tubing.

Tubing

See **tube**.

ISA Publications

Application Concepts of Process Control. P. W. Murrill. Instrument Society of America, Research Triangle Park, NC. 1988.
(ISBN: 1-55617-171-4)

Automatic Tuning of PID Controllers. K. J. Astrom and T. Hagglund. Instrument Society of America, Research Triangle Park, NC. 1988.
(ISBN: 1-55617-081-5)

Electronic Controllers. L. M. Thompson. Instrument Society of America, Research Triangle Park, NC. 1989.
(ISBN: 1-555617-129-3)

Flow Measurement. D. W. Spitzer, ed. Instrument Society of America, Research Triangle Park, NC. 1991.
(ISBN: 1-555617-334-2)

Fundamentals of Flow Measurement. J. P. DeCarlo. Instrument Society of America, Research Triangle Park, NC. 1984.
(ISBN: 0-087664-627-5)

Fundamentals of Process Control Theory., 2nd ed. P. W. Murrill. Instrument Society of America, Research Triangle Park, NC. 1981.
(ISBN: 0-87664-507-4)

Industrial Flow Measurement, 2nd ed. D. W. Spitzer. Instrument Society of America, Research Triangle Park, NC. 1990.
(ISBN: 1-555617-243-5)

Industrial Pressure Measurement. D. R. Gillum. Instrument Society of America, Research Triangle Park, NC. 1982.
(ISBN: 0-87664-668-2)

Measurement and Control of Liquid Level. C. H. Cho. Instrument Society of America, Research Triangle Park, NC. 1982.
(ISBN: 0-87664-625-9)

Process Control Fundamentals Package. Instrument Society of America, Research Triangle Park, NC. 1987.
(ISBN: 1-55617-195-1)

Temperature Measurement in Industry. E. C. Magison. Instrument Society of America, Research Triangle Park, NC. 1990.
(ISBN: 1-55617-208-7)

Bibliography

Standards and Recommended Practices

The Comprehensive Dictionary of Instrumentation and Control. Instrument Society of America, Research Triangle Park, NC. (ISBN: 1-55617-125-0)

ANSI/ISA-S5.1, *Instrumentation Symbols and Identification.* Instrument Society of America, Research Triangle Park, NC. 1984. (ISBN: 0-87664-844-8)

ANSI/ISA-S5.4, *Instrument Loop Diagrams.* Instrument Society of America, Research Triangle Park, NC. 1976 (Revised 1989). (ISBN: 1-55617-227-3)

ANSI/ISA-S5.5, *Graphic Symbols for Process Displays.* Instrument Society of America, Research Triangle Park, NC. 1985 (Approved 1986). (ISBN: 0-87664-935-5)

ANSI/ISA-RP12.6, *Installation of Intrinsically Safe Instrument Systems in Hazardous (Classified) Locations.* Instrument Society of America, Research Triangle Park, NC. 1977 (Revised 1987). (ISBN: 1-55617-082-3)

RP42.1, *Nomenclature for Instrument Tube Fittings.* Instrument Society of America, Research Triangle Park, NC. 1982. (ISBN: 0-87664-9733-6)

RP60.9, *Piping Guide for Control Centers.* Instrument Society of America, Research Triangle Park, NC. 1981. (ISBN: 0-87664-556-2)

ANSI/ISA-S51.1, *Process Instrumentation Terminology.* Instrument Society of America, Research Triangle Park, NC. 1979. (ISBN: 0-87664-390-4)

Videotapes

Instrumentation Video Series. Instrument Society of America, Research Triangle Park, NC. 1985, 1986, 1987, 1988.

Continuous Process Control Series. Instrument Society of America, Research Triangle Park, NC. 1989.

Control Technology and Application Series. Instrument Society of America, Research Triangle Park, NC. 1988.

Industrial Measurement Series. Instrument Society of America, Research Triangle Park, NC. 1987.

Bibliography

INVOLVE®
Interactive
Videodisc Instruction

Controller Tuning Series
Instrument Society of America, Research Triangle Park, NC. 1990.

Electronic Maintenance Series
Instrument Society of America, Research Triangle Park, NC. 1991.

Industrial Process Control Series
Instrument Society of America, Research Triangle Park, NC. 1991.

Interpreting Process Control Diagrams
Instrument Society of America, Research Triangle Park, NC. 1990.

Troubleshooting Series
Instrument Society of America, Research Triangle Park, NC. 1990.

Index

ISA

67 Alexander Drive

P.O. Box 12277

Research Triangle Park, NC

27709

WASHINGTON STATE COM 12/08/2008

MECHANICAL CONNECTIO

9781556173516 0000

9 781556 173516   NEW

T2-APE-643

ISBN 1-55617-35